Awesome
Math
Problems
FOR
Creative
Thinking

Linda Jensen Sheffield
Carole E. Greenes
Carol R. Findell
M. Katherine Gavin

Wright Group
McGraw-Hill

Acknowledgments

EDITOR Harriet Slonim

PROJECT EDITOR Janet Pittock

DESIGN DIRECTOR Karen Lee Stack

DESIGN Laurie Szujewska

COVER ILLUSTRATION Bonni Evensen

ILLUSTRATION Bonni Evensen

TYPESETTING Laurie Szujewska

©2000 Creative Publications, Inc.
One Prudential Plaza
Chicago, IL 60601

Creative Publications is a registered trademark.
Printed in the United States of America.
All rights reserved.

No part of this publication may be reproduced,
or copied into or stored in a retrieval system,
or transmitted, in any form or by any means,
electronic, mechanical, photocopying, recording,
or otherwise, without the prior written
permission of the publisher.

ISBN 0-7622-1285-3
Customer Service 800-624-0822
www.creativepublications.com
    5 6 7 8 QDB 11

THIS BOOK BELONGS TO:

_____

We wrote this book just for you. It's filled with our favorite problems. Some are hard. Others are really hard. Still others are really, *really* hard. (These are the ones at the end of the book.)

What's great about these problems is that when you do them you get to use what you know about math in different ways. And doing them will help you learn lots more about math, too. You can jot down ideas and solutions right in this book.

Take this book along with you everywhere. This way you can do the problems while you're traveling, at recess, watching TV, eating lunch, under the covers, and over e-mail. You get the picture. Just do 'em!

Have Fun!

Hidden Figures

How many 3-, 4-, 5-, and 6-sided figures do you see below?

Give yourself points for each one you find.

Here's how to score.

- 3 points for each Triangle
- 4 points for each Quadrilateral
- 5 points for each Pentagon
- 6 points for each Hexagon

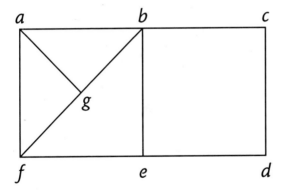

How many points did you get?

East of Eden

Tammy and Val are traveling west on Route 140 on their way to Huntsville. They have just passed a sign that says they are 22 miles east of Eden. Twenty-two miles is $\frac{1}{3}$ the distance from Eden to the intersection of Route 213. The signpost below is at the intersection of Route 140 and Route 213.

How many miles do Tommy and Val have left to go?

Technically Speaking

100 computer "techies" come to a conference. Each of them exchanges a business card with each of the others.

How many cards are exchanged?

Find Your Seat

The seat numbers in the Triangle Theater follow this pattern.

You are sitting in seat 399.

Which seat number is directly in front of you?

Know Your ABC's

Regions *A*, *B*, and *C* each contain a different number. The number in each circle is the sum of the numbers in the two adjacent regions.

What are the values of each of regions *A*, *B*, and *C*?

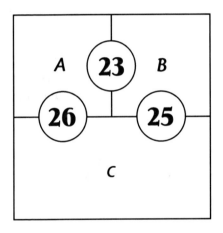

A = _____

B = _____

C = _____

It's Abundantly Clear!

How much greater is the greatest 2-digit prime number than the greatest 2-digit abundant number?

A number is *abundant* if the sum of its proper factors is greater than it is.

12 is abundant because 12 < 16. proper factors of 12: 1, 2, 3, 4, 6
1 + 2 + 3 + 4 + 6 = 16

All the factors of a number, except the number itself, are *proper factors*.

A number with exactly two factors, itself and 1, is a *prime number*.

Pick a Chip!

A bag contains 10 red, 10 blue, and 10 green chips.

What is the fewest chips of each color that should be removed from the bag so that the probability of picking red will be $\frac{2}{7}$ and the probability of picking blue will be $\frac{2}{7}$?

Try for Triangles

Get 9 same-size paper clips.
Arrange them to form five triangles.
The total area of four of the triangles must be equal to the area of the fifth triangle.

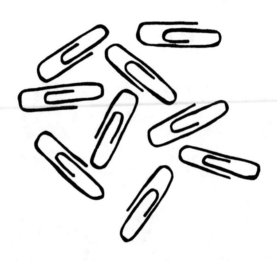

Multiplication = Addition

See how the *sum* of a pair of numbers can equal the *product* of the pair!

$2 + 2 = 4$

$2 \times 2 = 4$

$3 + 1\frac{1}{2} = 4\frac{1}{2}$

$3 \times 1\frac{1}{2} = 4\frac{1}{2}$

$10 + 1\frac{1}{9} = 11\frac{1}{9}$

$10 \times 1\frac{1}{9} = 11\frac{1}{9}$

Find five more pairs of numbers, each with the same sum and product.

Growing Triangles

Each figure below contains a different number of small triangles. Suppose the pattern continues.

How many more small triangles will there be in Figure 52 than in Figure 49?

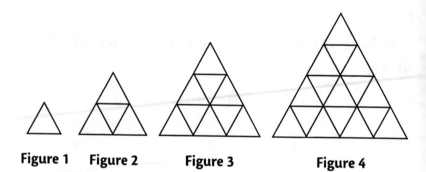

Figure 1   **Figure 2**   **Figure 3**   **Figure 4**

Heads Up!

A total of 18 animals are in a field.
Some are chickens, some are sheep, and some are cows.
The total number of legs is 10 more than three times
the total number of heads.

How many chickens are in the field?

Wait—
Just Find the Weight!

Same shapes have same weights.
Different shapes have different weights.

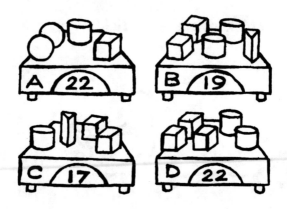

◯ weighs _____ pounds.

A Rollicking Ride

"There's the carousel!" I shouted back to Dad as I ran on ahead. (I can never resist a ride on a carousel horse.)

While Dad waited for me, he sketched this graph to show my ride.

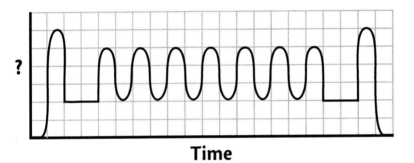

Time

What would be a good label for the vertical axis on the graph?

Building Blocks

My little sister used her alphabet blocks to build a wall 8 blocks long, 8 blocks high, and 2 blocks wide. This took her 8 minutes.

At this rate, how long would it take her to build a wall 4 blocks long, 4 blocks high, and 1 block wide?

Equivalent Fractions

Use each of the digits in the box just once.

$$1\ 2\ 3\ 4\ 5\ 6\ 7\ 8\ 9$$

Arrange the digits in the boxes below to form three equivalent fractions.

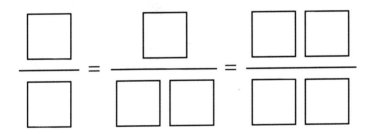

The Mystery Pair

The greatest common factor (GCF) of two numbers is 12.
The least common multiple (LCM) of the two is 144.
The sum of the two is less than 144.

What is the pair of numbers?

The *GCF* of two whole numbers
is the greatest number that is
a factor of both numbers.

The *LCM* of two numbers is the
smallest positive number that
is a multiple of both numbers.

Perplexing Palindromes

The difference between two 3-digit palindromes is 11.
The sum of the digits that make up the greater
palindrome is 18.

What are the two palindromes?

Palindromic Numbers—like
121 and 303—read the same
forward and backward.

What's the Difference?

These figures are made up of light squares and dark squares. Suppose the pattern continues.

In which figure will the difference between the numbers of dark squares and light squares be equal to 56?

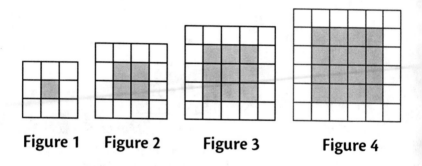

Figure 1   Figure 2   Figure 3   Figure 4

The Chicken Special

A bunch of us went to the Chicken Coop for dinner.
Some of us ordered chicken.
Some of us ordered apple pie.
Sixteen of us ordered milk.

This Venn diagram shows some of our orders.

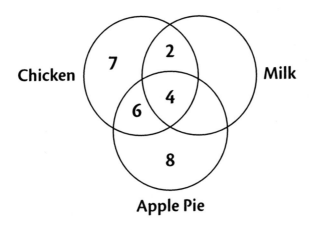

Complete the Venn diagram, then tell how many of us ordered just milk, just apple pie, or just milk *and* apple pie, but no chicken.

Macaroni and Cheese

Each week, Mrs. Mack buys exactly $3\frac{5}{8}$ pounds of cheese for her mac-and-cheese recipe. She chooses from these kinds of cheese.

Mrs. Mack buys as many packages as she needs— up to three packages of any one kind.

What packages of cheese (and how many of each kind) does Mrs. Mack buy?

American Cheese · $\frac{7}{8}$ lb

Cheddar Cheese · 0.5 lb

Swiss Cheese · 0.2 lb

Shady Cube

Here are three views of the same cube.

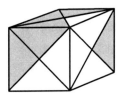 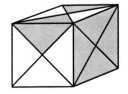 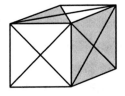

Someone started shading this net to match the cube above.

Complete the shading to show a net that could be folded to form the cube.

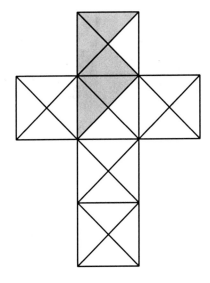

Party Time

Chris wants a hat and a noisemaker for each of the 39 people who are coming to his year-end party.

At the store, he sees two kinds of packages of hats and noisemakers. Chris figures how to get exactly as many hats and noisemakers as he needs by buying the right number of each kind of package.

How many blue packages should he buy?
How many green packages?

Target Practice

The radii of the circles on this dart board measure 2 cm, 4 cm, 6 cm, 8 cm, and 10 cm. Any dart thrown towards this board has equally likely chances of landing anywhere on it.

Which is greater, the probability of a dart landing on the gray region or the probability of it landing on the black region?

Five in a Row

The sum of five consecutive whole numbers is 90.

What is the greatest of these five numbers?

A Booming Business

Bill opened a bookstore and sold 2 books the first day,
6 books the second day, 10 books the third day,
14 books the fourth, 18 the fifth, and so on.
Business boomed! The sales pattern continued.

On what day did Bill sell 282 books?

What's Showing?

Evan picks up a 10 × 10 × 10 cube made of 1,000 unit cubes. He examines it on all 6 sides. He wonders how many more unit cubes it has with one face showing than with three faces showing.

How many more do you think it has?

Five-Digit Sentence

Use each of the digits 1 through 5 just once to make this multiplication statement true.

$$\boxed{}\ \boxed{} \times \boxed{} = \boxed{}\ \boxed{}$$

    a   *b*   *c*   *d*   *e*

What number is *de*?

Laughing All the Way

If a Hee + Hee + Haw is 10
and a Haw + Haw + Hee is 11,
how much is a Hee + Hee + Hee?

An Average of 12

I am thinking of three different positive numbers.
The greatest of them is twice a perfect square.
The least of them is 1 less than half the greatest.
The average of the three numbers is 12.

Which three numbers am I thinking of?

Average is another word for
the mean of a set of numbers.
Find the average by adding
the numbers in the set and
then dividing the sum by
the number of addends.

The Cherry Caper

A tempting bowlful of cherries was on the table. Sally came in from soccer practice and ate $\frac{1}{6}$ of the cherries. Sammy charged in from a game and ate $\frac{1}{5}$ of the those that were left. Later, Susie saw the bowl and ate $\frac{1}{4}$ of the cherries left in it. Dad ate $\frac{1}{3}$ of the remaining cherries while he and Mom made dinner. Then Mom ate $\frac{1}{2}$ of what was left. When the family sat down for dinner, 4 cherries remained in the bowl.

How many cherries did Sally eat?

Four in a Row

Choose from the numbers 12 through 17. Place them in the connected circles so that the numbers along each line have a sum of 50. **Do this in two different ways.**

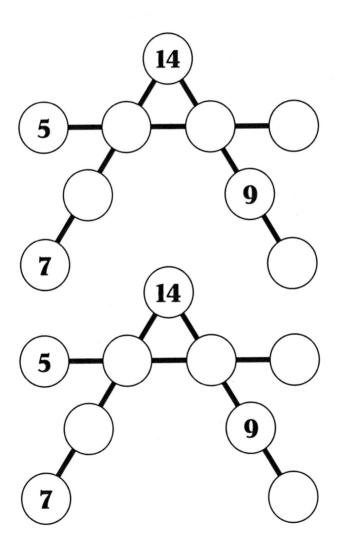

Find the Combination

Mr. Takaya remembered that all the digits in the combination to his office door lock were different, but he forgot what they were! At last he found a paper with clues to the combination that he'd written long ago.

Use these clues to help him unlock the door.

- a, b, and e are triangular numbers.
- b, c, and g are square numbers.
- d, e, f, and j are prime numbers.
- a, d, g, h, and i are even numbers.
- $e + j = h$

a	b	c
d	e	f
g	h	i
	j	

HINT

A whole number greater than 1 that has just two factors, itself and 1, is a *prime number*.

The product of any number and itself is a *square number*.

The set of numbers generated by triangular arrays of dots (1, 3, 6, 10, ...) are the *triangular numbers*.

Fractions of x

$$\frac{1}{2}x + \frac{1}{3}x + \frac{1}{4}x + \frac{1}{5}x = 77$$

What is the value of x?

"Square" Target

Imagine three darts landing on this target.

If the sum of values of the regions in which they land is a square number, in what different ways can they land?

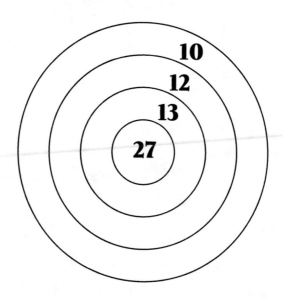

A Valuable Rectangle

Same shapes have same numbers.
Different shapes have different numbers.
Complete the number sentences.

$$3 \times \triangle = \bigcirc$$

$$\bigcirc + \triangle - \square = -1$$

$$\triangle + \square + \bigcirc = 17$$

What is the value of $\square$ **?**

Where is 419?

Pretend that the pattern continues.

Row 1	1	2							
Row 2	3	4	5	6					
Row 3	7	8	9	10	11	12			
Row 4	13	14	15	16	17	18	19	20	
Row 5	21	22	23	24	25	26	27	28	29	30

In which row is 419? Where is it in the row?

The Midas Touch

Pretend the square piece of gold shown here is worth $1,000. *A* and *B* are the midpoints of each of their sides.

What would be the value of the shaded part of the gold?

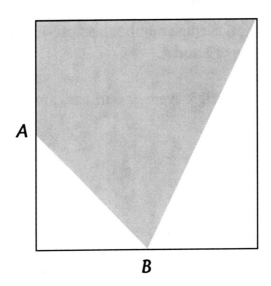

It's Just Average

A three-digit number in which one digit is the average of the other two digits is called an *average number*.

For example:

- 456 is an average number because 5 is the average of 4 and 6.

- 426 is an average number because 4 is the average of 2 and 6.

How many three-digit average numbers are there?

What an Illusion!

In this diagram, segment *AB* is parallel to line *s*.

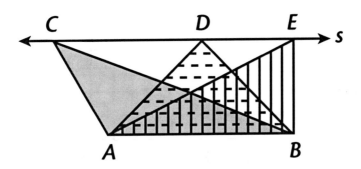

Which triangle has the greatest area?

Square Frenzy

Each figure below contains a different number of small squares. Suppose the pattern continues.

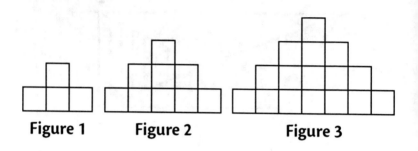

Figure 1   Figure 2   Figure 3

How many squares will there be in Figure 100?

Write On!

For $5 you can buy 7 pens and 5 notebooks or 9 pens and 3 notebooks.

At the same unit price, what is the total for 2 pens and 1 notebook?

Favorite Number

Three people each record a favorite number, either 1, 2, 3, or 4.

What is the probability that no two people have the same number?

Gear Up!

Gears are pairs of toothed wheels.
One wheel is usually bigger than the other.
Suppose Gear A, with 6 teeth, turns clockwise 12 times.
As it turns, its teeth fit into the teeth of Gear B making
Gear B turn 9 times.

Gear A   Gear B

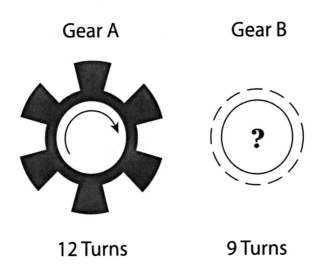

12 Turns   9 Turns

How many teeth does Gear B have? In which direction does it turn?

Raffle Baffle

The athletic club held a raffle. They sold a whole batch of tickets at $1 apiece. Every ticket had a 3-digit number from 000 to 999 and all possible 3-digit numbers were represented equally. One number was picked and each person holding a ticket for that exact 3-digit number won $500.

If the club sold 5,000 tickets, how much did they pay the winners?

Shape Puzzle

Same shapes have same numbers.
Different shapes have different numbers.
Complete the number sentences.

$$\bigcirc + \square - \triangle = 11$$

$$\bigcirc + \triangle + \triangle = 9$$

$$\square - \triangle = 6$$

What is the value of $\bigcirc + \square$ **?**

Moving Means...

Move two of the numbers from one group to another so that the numbers in each group have the same *mean*, or average.

Group 1
47　56
82　97

Group 2
40　58　72
52　90

Group 3
78　62　85
45　68　43

Mean—The average of a set of numbers found by adding the numbers in the set and then dividing the sum by the number of addends.

Rectangle Ruckus

Help! I started to arrange the numbers from 1 through 16 in the boxes to match the sums of the columns and rows. But now I'm stuck.

Please find the missing numbers.
(And don't forget that missing sum in the last row!)

7	14			**28**
13			15	**40**
	8		6	**27**
				_____
34	**32**	**32**	**38**	

1 2 3 4 5 ~~6~~ ~~7~~ ~~8~~ 9 10 11 12 ~~13~~ ~~14~~ ~~15~~ 16

Off Balance

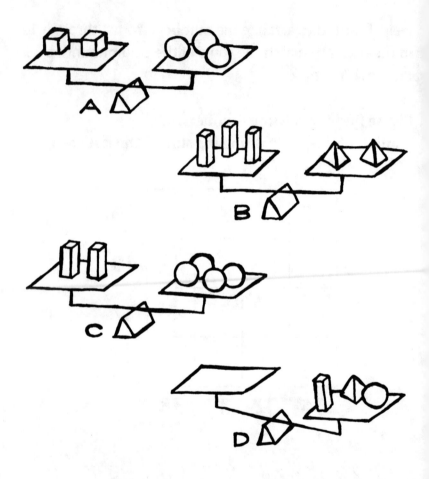

How many would you need to balance scale D?

Two Cubes

The sum of the lengths of the edges of cube A and cube B is a square number of inches. The sum of the volumes of the cubes is a square number between 500 and 600. Cube B is larger than cube A.

What are the dimensions of cube B?

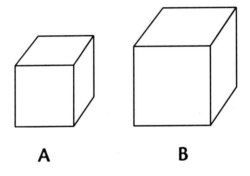

A   B

How many edges does
a cube have?

An Odd Request

Use all the odd numbers (1, 3, 5, 7, and 9) and any operations to form equations equal to each of the even numbers from 2 to 20. The first one is done for you.

$\dfrac{9-7}{5-3} + 1$	=	2
	=	4
	=	6
	=	8
	=	10
	=	12
	=	14
	=	16
	=	18
	=	20

Answers ☀ ☀ ☀ ☀ ☀ ☀ ☀ ☀ ☀ ☀ ☀ ☀

An Average of 12

18, 10, and 8

A Booming Business

71st day;

Each day, the number of books sold
was 4 times the number of days
minus 2. (For example, on the third
day he sold 10 books because 4×3,
or 12, minus 2, equals 10.) If d stands
for the number of days, then
282 books = $4 \times d - 2$ and $d = 71$.

Building Blocks

1 minute;

Eight $4 \times 4 \times 1$ regions make up
the $8 \times 8 \times 2$ wall.

Since the $4 \times 4 \times 1$ region is
$\frac{1}{8}$ the size of the $8 \times 8 \times 2$ wall,
it would take $\frac{1}{8}$ of 8 minutes,
or 1 minute, to build it.

The Cherry Caper

4 cherries;

Before Sally ate some cherries, there
were 24. She ate $\frac{1}{6}$ of 24, or 4.

That left 20. Sammy ate $\frac{1}{5}$ of 20, or 4.

That left 16. Susie ate $\frac{1}{4}$ of 16, or 4.

That left 12. Dad ate $\frac{1}{3}$ of 12, or 4.

That left 8. Mom ate $\frac{1}{2}$ of 8, or 4.

That left 4.

The Chicken Special

18;

The shaded parts represent orders
of just milk or just apple pie or milk
and apple pie, but no chicken—
10 + 8 = 18.

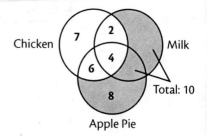

East of Eden

136 miles;

22 is $\frac{1}{3}$ of 66, so they need to go 22 mi to get to Eden, then 66 mi from Eden to Route 213, and 48 mi from Route 213 to Huntsville. 22 + 66 + 48 = 136

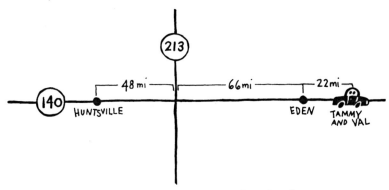

Equivalent Fractions

Two possible solutions include

$$\frac{3}{6} = \frac{9}{1\boxed{8}} = \frac{2\boxed{7}}{5\boxed{4}}$$

and

$$\frac{3}{6} = \frac{7}{1\boxed{4}} = \frac{2\boxed{9}}{5\boxed{8}}$$

Favorite Number

$\frac{24}{64}$, or $\frac{3}{8}$; The first person has a $\frac{4}{4}$ chance of picking any of the numbers, the second person has a $\frac{3}{4}$ chance of picking a different number than the first person, and the third person then has a $\frac{2}{4}$ chance of picking yet a different number.

$\frac{4}{4} \times \frac{3}{4} \times \frac{2}{4} = \frac{24}{64}$, or $\frac{3}{8}$.

Find the Combination

6	1	9
a	b	c
2	3	7
d	e	f
4	8	0
g	h	i
	5	
	j	

Answers ✺✺✺✺✺✺✺✺✺✺✺✺

Find Your Seat
361;
The number of the last seat in each row is equal to (Row Number)². Seat 400 is at the end of Row 20. Seat 399 is just to the left of seat 400. In front of seat 399 is the last seat in Row 19, which is 19², or 361.

Five in a Row
20;
Divide 90 by 5 to get 18, so 18 is the middle number of the five. Then the five numbers with a sum of 90 are 16, 17, 18, 19, and 20.

Five-Digit Sentence
52;

| 1 | 3 | × | 4 | = | 5 | 2 |
| a | b | | c | | d | e |

Four in a Row
Here are three solutions.

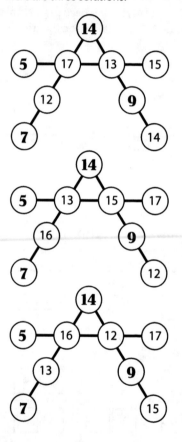

Fractions of x
$x = 60$;
$\frac{1}{2}$ of 60 is 30.
$\frac{1}{3}$ of 60 is 20.
$\frac{1}{4}$ of 60 is 15.
$\frac{1}{5}$ of 60 is 12.
30 + 21 + 15 + 12 = 77, so $x = 60$.

Gear Up!

Gear B has 8 teeth.

It turns counterclockwise;

The more teeth a gear has, the fewer turns it makes. This is because there is an inverse, or opposite, relationship between the number of teeth and the number of turns. So,

$$\frac{\text{Teeth (Gear A)}}{\text{Teeth (Gear B)}} = \frac{\text{Turns (Gear B)}}{\text{Turns (Gear A)}}$$

$$\frac{6}{x} = \frac{9}{12}$$

$$9x = 72$$

$$x = 8$$

Growing Triangles

303;

Find the number of triangles in Figures 50, 51, and 52.

If n = Figure Number, then the bottom row of each figure has $2n - 1$ small triangles.

Figure 52 $2(52) - 1 = 103$
Figure 51 $2(51) - 1 = 101$
Figure 50 $2(50) - 1 = \underline{\hphantom{0}99}$
                  Total = 303

or

Each figure is made up of (Figure Number)^2 triangles. So, Figure 52 has 52^2, or 2,704 triangles and Figure 49 has 49^2, or 2,401 triangles.

$2{,}704 - 2{,}401 = 303$ triangles.

Heads Up!

4 chickens;

There are 64 legs in all—

3×18 (heads) $+ 10 = 64$ legs.

If all 18 animals were 4-legged, then there would be 72 legs. But 72 is 8 legs more than 64, so 4 of the animals must be (2-legged) chickens.

$4 \times 2 + 14 \times 4 = 8 + 56 = 64$ legs.

Hidden Figures

49 points;

There are four triangles—
abg, agf, abf, bef.

There are four quadrilaterals—
acdf, abef, bcde, bcdf.

There are three pentagons—
acdfg, abefg, afebg.

There is one hexagon—*agbcdf.*

That gives you

$(4 \times 3) + (4 \times 4) + (3 \times 5) + (1 \times 6)$

or 49 points.

It's Abundantly Clear!

1;

The greatest 2-digit prime number is 97.

The greatest 2-digit abundant number is 96.

$97 - 96 = 1$

Answers ✺✺✺✺✺✺✺✺✺✺✺✺

It's Just Average
121;

Average of 1 (5 numbers)
111
102 (4 arrangements)

Average of 2 (11 numbers)
222
213 (6 arrangements)
204 (4 arrangements)

Average of 3 (17 numbers)
333
315 (6 arrangements)
324 (6 arrangements)
306 (4 arrangements)

Average of 4 (23 numbers)
444
435 (6 arrangements)
426 (6 arrangements)
417 (6 arrangements)
408 (4 arrangements)

Average of 5 (25 numbers)
555
546 (6 arrangements)
537 (6 arrangements)
528 (6 arrangements)
519 (6 arrangements)

Average of 6 (19 numbers)
666
657 (6 arrangements)
648 (6 arrangements)
639 (6 arrangements)

Average of 7 (13 numbers)
777
768 (6 arrangements)
759 (6 arrangements)

Average of 8 (7 numbers)
888
879 (6 arrangements)

Average of 9 (1 number)
999

Know Your ABC's
$A = 12$
$B = 11$
$C = 14$

Laughing All the Way
9;

Since Hee + Hee + Haw is 10 and Haw + Haw + Hee is 11, then the sum of Hee + Hee + Haw and Haw + Haw + Hee is 21. That means 3 Hee's and 3 Haw's are 21, so Hee + Haw must be 21 ÷ 3, or 7. If Hee + Haw is 7, and Hee + Hee + Haw is 10, then the extra Hee must be 3. That means Hee + Hee + Hee is 3×3, or 9.

Macaroni and Cheese
3 packages of American cheese and 2 packages of cheddar;

American cheese:
$3 \times \frac{7}{8} = \frac{21}{8} = 2\frac{5}{8}$ pounds
Cheddar: $2 \times 0.5 = 1$ pound
Total: $2\frac{5}{8} + 1 = 3\frac{5}{8}$ pounds

The Midas Touch

$625;

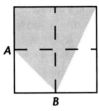

First find the value of the unshaded part of the piece of gold. The dotted lines shown here divide the piece into fourths. Then the unshaded triangle at left is $\frac{1}{8}$ of the whole piece, worth $125. And the unshaded triangle at right is $\frac{1}{4}$ of the whole piece, worth $250. $1,000 − $250 = $750 and $750 − $125 = $625.

Moving Means...

Move 78 from Group 3 to Group 2 and move 43 from Group 3 to Group 1;
New Group 1: 43, 47, 56, 82, 97
New Group 2: 40, 52, 58, 72, 78, 90
New Group 3: 45, 62, 68, 85
The average of each new group is 65.

Multiplication = Addition

There are many possible solutions. Here is one.
$5 + 1\frac{1}{4} = 6\frac{1}{4}$ and $5 \times 1\frac{1}{4} = 6\frac{1}{4}$
This formula will help you find other solutions.
$$n \times (1 + \tfrac{1}{(n-1)}) = n + (1 + \tfrac{1}{(n-1)})$$

The Mystery Pair

36 and 48

An Odd Request

Here are some possible solutions.
$(9 + 5 − 7 − 3) \times 1 = 4$
$(9 − 3) \times (7 − 5 − 1) = 6$
$(9 − 1) \times (5 + 3 − 7) = 8$
$(9 + 1) \times (5 + 3 − 7) = 10$
$(9 + 3) \times (7 − 5 − 1) = 12$
$(5 \times 3) − (9 − 7 − 1) = 14$
$(5 + 3) \times (9 − 7) \times 1 = 16$
$(5 + 3 + 1) \times (9 − 7) = 18$
$(7 − 3) \times (9 − 5 + 1) = 20$

Off Balance

4 cubes;
On scale C, 1 rectangular solid balances 2 spheres.
On scale B, substitute 2 spheres for each rectangular solid. Then 1 pyramid balances 3 spheres.
On scale D, substitute 3 spheres for the pyramid. Substitute 2 spheres for the rectangular solid. That leaves 6 spheres on the right side of the balance.
On scale A, 2 cubes balance 3 spheres, so to balance 6 spheres, place 4 cubes on the left side of the balance.

Party Time

2 blue packages and 3 green packages;
Two blue packages have 12 hats and 18 noisemakers. Three green packages have 27 hats and 21 noisemakers. Together, two blue packages and three green packages give you 39 hats and 39 noisemakers.

Answers ✹✹✹✹✹✹✹✹✹✹✹✹

Perplexing Palindromes

898 and 909; A difference of 11 occurs only when the hundreds digit changes, as in 202 − 191. The sum of the digits of the greater palindrome is 18, so the greater palindrome must be 909. Subtract 898 from 909 and you get a difference of 11.

Pick a Chip!

4 blue, 4 red, and 1 green should be removed. When 4 red, 4 blue, and 1 green chip are removed, the bag contains 6 red, 6 blue, and 9 green chips, for a total of 21 chips. The probability of picking red or picking blue is $\frac{6}{21}$, or $\frac{2}{7}$.

Raffle Baffle

$2,500;

There are 1,000 3-digit numbers from 000 to 999. 5,000 tickets were sold in all, so 5 tickets had the winning number. The club paid each of the 5 winners $500, for a total of $2,500.

Rectangle Ruckus

7	14	2	5	28
13	1	11	15	49
10	8	3	6	27
4	9	16	12	41
34	32	32	38	

A Rollicking Ride

"Distance of Rider's Feet from Ground"; The vertical axis is the distance of the rider's feet from the ground as the rider first walks onto the carousel and gets up on the horse, while the horse moves up and down, as the carousel slows to a stop, as the rider dismounts, and when the rider walks away.

Shady Cube

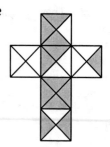

Shape Puzzle

⑤ + ⑧ = 13

⑤ + ⑧ − △2 = 11

⑤ + △2 + △2 = 9

⑧ − △2 = 6

Square Frenzy

101^2, or 10,201 squares;
Figure 1 has 2^2, or 4 squares.
Figure 2 has 3^2, or 9 squares.
Figure 3 has 4^2, or 16 squares.
Figure 4 has 5^2, or 25 squares.
Figure n has $(n + 1)^2$ squares.

"Square" Target
10, 12, 27   27, 27, 27
13, 13, 10   27, 27, 10
12, 12, 12

Target Practice
Both are equally likely;
Area of gray region = $\pi(6)^2 = 36\pi$
Area of black region =
$\pi(10)^2 - \pi(8)^2 = 100\pi - 64\pi = 36\pi$

Technically Speaking
9,900 cards; Each computer techie
exchanges a card with 99 others,
so the number of cards is
$100 \times 99 = 9,900$.

Try for Triangles

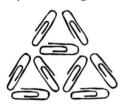

Two Cubes
8 in. $\times$ 8 in. $\times$ 8 in.;
Cube A measures 4 in. $\times$ 4 in. $\times$ 4 in.
Cube B measures 8 in. $\times$ 8 in. $\times$ 8 in.
Each cube has 12 edges. Total edge
length of cube A: 4×12, or 48 inches.
Total edge length of cube B: 8×12, or
96 in. The sum of the lengths of the
edges of both cubes is 48 + 96, or
144 in. Volume of cube A: 4^3, or 64 in³.
Volume of cube B: 8^3, or 512 in³. Sum
of the volumes of the cubes is 576 in³.

A Valuable Rectangle

☐ = **9**

3 × △⟨2⟩ = ⬤6

⬤6 + △⟨2⟩ − ☐9 = −1

△⟨2⟩ + ☐9 + ⬤6 = 17

Wait—Just Find the Weight!
7 pounds; All the shapes on scale C
are on scale B. So subtract all the
shapes on C from B,

leaving 1 ⬡ = 2.

On scale D, replace each ⬡ with 2.
The 3 ⬡⬡ = 18, so ⬡⬡ = 6.

On scale A, replace ⬡⬡ with 6 and
⬡ with 2. The 2 ◗ = 14, so
◗ = 7.

Answers ✺✺✺✺✺✺✺✺✺✺✺✺

What an Illusion!

They all have the same area;

Use the formula for the area of a triangle $(A = \frac{1}{2}bh)$, where b = base of a triangle and h = height. Since the base and height are the same for all the triangles, the triangles must all have the same area.

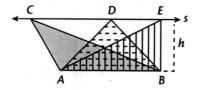

What's Showing?

376 unit cubes;

On each face of the thousands cube all the unit cubes, except for those along the edges, have one face showing. So each face has 8 × 8, or 64, unit cubes with one face showing. The thousands cube has 6 faces for a total of 6 × 64, or 384, unit cubes with one face showing. Each of the 8 corner cubes has 3 faces showing. So subtract: 384 − 8 = 376.

What's the Difference?

Figure 10;

The number of dark squares increases from one figure to the next by adding the odd numbers in order (1, 3, 5, 7, ...). The number of light squares increases from one figure to the next by the addition of 4. Find the difference between the number of dark squares and light squares in each figure. In Figure 10, there are 100 dark squares and 44 light squares, with a difference of 56.

Where is 419?

419 is the next-to-last number in Row 20;

The last number in each row is equal to the row number squared plus the row number (R^2 + R). That's why the last number in Row 5 is (5^2 + 5), or 30. The last number in Row 20 is (20^2 + 20), or 400 + 20 = 420. So 419 is in second from the end of row 20.

Write On!

$1.25;

With $10 you can buy 16 pens and 8 notebooks.

8 × (2 pens + 1 notebook) = $10

$10 ÷ 8 = $1.25